BETTER
THAN
BLENDED
WORKBOOK

BETTER THAN BLENDED WORKBOOK
A Study to Help Blended Families Grow Closer to
Each Other and Closer to God

BY WILLIE AND RACHEL G. SCOTT

TKI TEAM KINGDOM IMPACT PUBLISHING

A Better Than Blended Family Ministries book published by Team Kingdom Impact Publishing, LLC.

PO Box 18699
Cleveland Heights, OH 44118

The material in appendix 1 is from HelpGuide.org and is used by permission.

Printed in the United States of America
24 23 22 21 20 19 18 17 16 1 2 3 4 5 6

ISBN-13 (trade paper): 978-0-9973626-7-1
Library of Congress Control Number: 2016903606

Editor: Rebecca English of Gladbooks Editorial Services
Cover design by Jesus Cordero
Back Cover Photo by Autumn Scott

"Children are a gift from the LORD; they are a reward from him" (Psalm 127:3).

We are thankful that God not only rewarded us greatly with children but also blessed us to overflowing with amazing children.

Antonio, Willie III, Autumn, Dominique, Darius, Aaron, and Gabrielle, we love you!

CONTENTS

Foreword by Jim and Jennifer Wilkes, Pastors of Journey Community Church

Preface: Welcome to Better than Blended

1. Writing Our Own Blended Family Stories...... 15

2. Dealing with Conflict 33

3. Better than Mended 53

4. Figuring Out Our Roles 71

5. Discipline Means Discipleship................... 91

6. Making Time for Family

   Togetherness 109

Appendix 1. How Different Ages Affect Children's Adjustment to Blended Families 135

Appendix 2. How Different Stages of Identity Affect Children's Adjustment to Blended Families................. 137

Leader's Guide 127

Notes 139

Resources 140

FOREWORD

By Jim and Jennifer Wilkes, Pastors of Journey Community Church

As pastors, we're always looking for tools and resources to help families in our church grow together in their faith. While there are plenty of curriculums and tools available for families, we haven't found many that are focused on helping blended families process and work through the unique challenges they're presented with. When Willie and Rachel shared with us their vision for Better than Blended, we were ecstatic and asked if they would lead a workshop at our church.

After the workshop ended, we received an e-mail from one of the attendees, who raved about the impact the workshop had on her marriage and in her family. She said she had grown in her individual relationship with God and was empowered to cultivate growth and spirituality in her family.

The Better than Blended curriculum provides blended families with practical steps to take to build relational equity, focus on Christ-centered principles, and foster a healthy home environment. As pastors, we can't think of a more important thing for a family to focus on than unity in Christ.

The Better than Blended curriculum is a must for those who are working toward bringing their once-separate families together. Whether you're already a blended family or about to become one, we believe this workbook will help you achieve greater unity and wholeness.

We believe in Better than Blended!

Pastors Jim and Jennifer Wilkes
Journey Community Church

PREFACE
WELCOME TO BETTER THAN BLENDED

When two people meet and fall in love, they typically don't take the time to fully consider the extent to which their love will change their lives. During a beautiful marriage ceremony, they stand before witnesses and confess their undying love and vow their commitment to one another. All the decorations and ceremonial pomp, however, don't prepare them for the hard work that lies ahead.

This is especially true for couples whose marriage will create a blended family—a joining together of his children and her children into one new family. Blended families bring to the altar hopes and dreams of a family that will become one. But those hopes and dreams can be dashed by the reality that getting the whole family on board with the couple's love isn't as easy as saying "I do" and then "you do too."

This was our story. As children we both experienced life in a blended family home and were exposed to the challenges of being in a blended family at an early age. When we joined together in marriage (Willie had three children, and Rachel had two), we prayed to be better than the blended families that we had experienced growing up. We desired to become one family! This was an audacious prayer—but God answered it. We now have a total of seven children ranging in age from infant to adult. Our testimony as one family has led to the birth of our ministry, Better than Blended, and become a catalyst toward redemption for blended families who are struggling to find common ground.

Our story is full of wisdom that we have gained through both mistakes and victories, and we want to share that wisdom with you.

We also want to encourage you that blending into the family that God has called you to be, even when the path gets difficult, is possible.

It is a journey—one that will have some steep valleys of seeming defeat as well as high mountains of apparent victories. But it is worth it!

Strong blended families aren't the result of some magic pill or a single prayer. Strong blended families take Word, work, and wisdom! We pray that you will find all of them in this study. This workbook presents a combination of applying the Word of God to your lives, learning to be intentional in creating effective family practices, and using God-given wisdom to move your family from simply being blended to being *better than blended.*

What does it mean to be better than blended? It means more than surviving—it means thriving! It means becoming a blended family that is actually one. It means becoming a family that is a pillar of strength and that develops an awesome testimony to the sustaining power of God's truth.

As you and your spouse begin and complete the *Better than Blended Workbook*, we would love to see three main goals achieved:

1. Enhance your blended family experience through drawing closer to God as a family

2. Strengthen your blended family by helping your children develop heartfelt relationships with each other for the future

3. Encourage you to be *intentional* about developing unity and oneness in every aspect of your blended family

This study is a curriculum for couples seeking to raise blended families in a unified and godly manner, but it is more than that. It is a template for you and your spouse to create and chronicle your story together and to share your testimony with other couples in a way that will help you see God's power moving in your life. Be ready to share this resource with another couple when you've completed it!

The workbook contains six sessions designed to be completed over a six-week period (each spouse should have his or her own workbook). It is intended to be done in a group setting with a leader (you will find a leader's guide at the back of this workbook), but it could just as easily be done with a few couples gathering or even with one couple at home. Each session is intended to last approximately an hour and a half and is broken into three sections:

1. Discovery (30 to 45 minutes): Consider what God is saying to you.

2. Discussion (30 to 45 minutes): Talk with your spouse and other couples about how what you've discovered applies to your situation.

3. Application (at home): What will we do differently now in our family?

Wherever you are as a blended family, if you as a couple desire unity and oneness, then engaging in this training with open hearts and minds will take your family to the next level. We pray that a deepened sense of God's call for your family will take root in your hearts and that the fruit of your love for each other, your children, and God will yield a family that is better than blended.

WRITING OUR OWN BLENDED FAMILY STORIES

Trust in the LORD with all your heart; do not depend on your own understanding. Seek his will in all you do, and he will show you which path to take.

Proverbs 3:5–6

Whether you are on the road to becoming a blended-family, have just become a blended family, or have been part of a blended family for many years, you have probably at one time or other asked, "How does this work?" Chances are, you hope for or have worked for a smooth transition and a happy family life for you, your spouse, and your children, but you also know that things are not always that easy. Adjusting to married life can be a big challenge in itself, but when we add children to the mix, things can become a lot more complicated.

So many things have been taught and suggested about how to become a blended family. In all likelihood, we've all heard well-meaning comments from people like, "It's so great that you'll be able to fill a parental void in your stepchildren's lives!" or "Your kids must be so excited to have new siblings!" or "Your family will be just like *The Brady Bunch*." Many of the things we hear, however, are myths, opinions, or simply speculations.

Not only do other people's opinions affect our outlook, but our own expectations can also derail us when it comes to what we think our blended family experience should be like. The way we were raised, especially if we ourselves grew up in a blended family, often forms much of our perspective as to how we think our family will function.

The fact is, none of people's various ideas nor our own past experiences can explain exactly what our blended-family experience should look like.

Becoming a blended family has its fair share of challenges, but it is possible to navigate this journey well and gracefully. The truth is, with God's help and some intentional effort on our part, we can create a unified family, no matter what others say or do and no matter what our own experiences were.

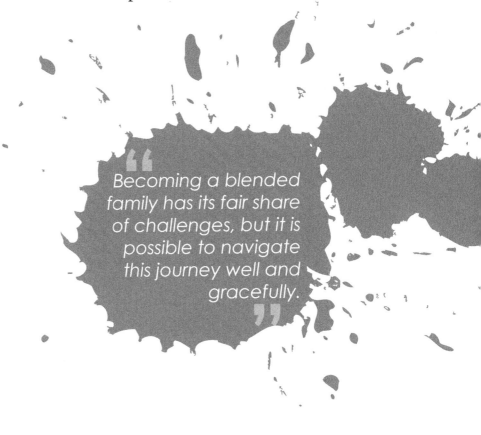

> Becoming a blended family has its fair share of challenges, but it is possible to navigate this journey well and gracefully.

DISCOVERY
CONSIDER WHAT GOD IS SAYING TO YOU

CREATING OUR OWN STORY—GOD'S WAY

All of us have developed ideologies about being a blended family, whether they are based on others' ideas or on our own past experiences. It is important for us to identify any false expectations that we hold and remove them from our minds so that we can start over with a clean slate and write a new story for our own blended family.

OTHER PEOPLE'S OPINIONS SHAPE OUR IDEOLOGIES

Stories and advice from others do not make up *your* story. When it comes to ideologies about blended families, we really can't debunk them, because the ideas may be true for some people. What we *can* do, however, is determine, no matter where we may be in blending our family, that we want to create our own story. It is okay to glean wisdom from other people's stories, because we may gain some needed light from them in certain areas of our family, but taking their stories and owning them for ourselves is a mistake that we can easily make. Stories and advice from other people are not your story.

One of the primary features of being a blended family is all the potential outside influences that can affect the process of a family becoming one. Ex-husbands or ex-wives, former in-laws, or any other affiliation from previous relationships can potentially affect the blending process. Yet the blessing in being a blended family is a chance to start fresh and new—to create new memories, traditions, and ways of life. New norms are often the result of blending a family, and in many cases it's a chance to start your story over.

Today is the day to start your story! Your story will not be based on your past or on what others have told you but on what you desire your blended family to become.

"Today is the day to start your story!"

OUR OWN EXPERIENCES SHAPE OUR EXPECTATIONS

We all have a story that, if revealed, would explain a lot about who we are now. For those of us who have experienced being in a blended family, we can't help but shape our expectations around what we know. For those who haven't been in a blended family, your expectations may be shaped around what you have heard or assume things will be like. Either experience is a good place to start, but remember this: *our experiences shape our expectations.*

One of the first steps toward writing our own family's story is to identify what we expect our blended family to look, feel, and act like. We need to identify what expectations we have—which may or may not be realistic—and the basis for them.

In doing that, we need to remember that how we grew up affects the way we view blending. Sometimes we don't notice how our upbringing influences our current family interactions or decisions, but it's important for us to recognize that it's a major factor.

As we look back at our childhood and identify the reasons behind our expectations, it will greatly help us in our blending process, because it will help us to identify which of our expectations are realistic and which may not be. Sometimes we have created massive expectations in order to guard our hearts from the unknown, and this can be detrimental to the goal of family oneness. We need to be open to our own blended family walk, however the journey may look.

THE RIGHT WAY TO BLEND

The truth is, there is no *perfect way* to blend, but there is a right way: *God's way!*

God isn't caught by surprise by our blended-family way of life. We can't help but think that the Creator of the world has a way in which He desires us to blend that will bring Him glory.

Although divorce ultimately is not God's will, He understands that allowing people to have free will puts a lot of hearts in a place where they may or may not be willing to work through things. Sometimes, although not all the time, God will release a person from a marriage that is not bringing Him glory. In other cases our youthful choices or extenuating circumstances led us to where we are now, or perhaps we arrived here with a widowed heart that still desires to love.

No matter what our story is, God's grace toward us is abundantly sufficient. It is through leaning on Him and intentionally seeking His guidance that He "will show [us] which path to take" (Proverbs 3:5–6) as it pertains to our families.

CREATING FAMILY UNITY

God's way of blending leads to family unity—but it requires some intentionality on our part.

Have you ever been talking to someone and had to explain the "yours, mine, and ours" scenario? It looks a little like this: "Well, Joe was mine before I remarried, and Bill had two kids from his previous marriage, and then we had one together." We always seem to end with an awkward pause and a half smile. Especially if the kids are standing there. And all the person asked is if all these kids were ours.

How do we think our stepchildren feel when we go through this long explanation? Especially if one of their birth parents isn't in their lives? What if they want to look at us as a parent?

This has happened to us (Willie and Rachel) on one too many occasions, but we decided early on that we would eliminate all the blended-family jargon unless it was absolutely necessary. Most of the time people have no idea that we are a blended family. It's not because all our kids call us Mom and Dad or because we all look alike but because if people ever ask if they are our children, our first and most common response is yes.

We don't go into a long explanation—we just leave it there.

If we want to blend God's way, we need to remember this: being better than blended means taking every step possible to create unity where division would desire to creep in. We have to ask God for help and then be intentional about becoming one as a family.

Being better than blended means taking every step possible to create unity where division would desire to creep in.

25

If our goal is to become a unified family, then the cliché of "yours, mine, and ours" must be addressed. "Yours" and "mine" should be removed so that "ours" stands alone. It is almost impossible for us to begin to develop a relationship with our stepchildren if we create a clear separation between our kids and our spouse's kids. We have to remember that although the children may be our spouse's, they are our God-given assignment to help raise. Our spouse is no longer in this boat alone, and neither are we.

You see, children know when we are not fully invested in building a relationship with them. Learning to embrace them all as "ours" breaks down the walls and shows our kids that regardless of when *they* decide to embrace our blended family, we are already committed. This is God's way! And our kids need to see this.

Yes, our hearts may get broken and our feelings may get hurt a few times. It may feel as if we're swimming upstream, and we're tired and would prefer to simply go with the flow. But we can take comfort in knowing that one day our children will be wiser and will look back at our relationship and truly know that we were always there for them—and that we not only spoke about God but also lived out our faith.

That's the message that we want them to see.

DISCUSSION:

HOW DOES THIS APPLY TO OUR SITUATION?

It's time to talk about what we've learned! Pair up with one or two other couples to answer and then discuss the questions below. (If you are uncomfortable talking with others or if you are doing this study at home, you can do this section with just your spouse.) Take ten to fifteen minutes to write your answers individually to the questions below, and then take an additional twenty to thirty minutes to discuss your answers with your spouse and the others in your group.

1. What are some wrong ideologies that you believe or have believed in the past about being a blended family?

2. What does having a clean slate look like for you?

3. Based on your own past experience, what expectations might you have about becoming a blended family?

4. What do you love about your family dynamic? What are some challenges that you face right now in becoming one family?

5. How have you learned to embrace "ours"? If you haven't, what is holding you back?

APPLICATION:

WHAT WILL WE DO DIFFERENTLY NOW?

Session 1 focused on discovering your own blended-family story. This week at home, before coming back for session 2 next week, set aside some time to complete the action activity below as a couple.

Each spouse should be allowed to explain his or her thoughts regarding the following questions and/ or activities. Speak honestly. Listen to each other respectfully.

1. Honestly assess your family and then decide which of the following statements best describes your situation:

   Two separate families

   Fluctuating between blended and separate

   One blended family

2. Based on your answers, what is one goal that you as a couple have for your family? Record your goal in the space below.

As you wrap up your application time together as a couple, spend some time in prayer together about the goal for your family that you recorded above. We have provided a specific prayer to meet you where you are as you finish session 1.

You can close with a prayer of your own, or you can use this one:

Dear Lord,

Thank You for bringing us together as a couple. Help us to see Your divine purpose in every aspect of our family. Let us look to You for guidance and direction as we seek to become one family in You. Help us to treat both our family's opportunities for growth and our family's successes with the same enthusiasm. Help our family members to be intentional and purposeful in our interactions with each other, treating one another as You would treat us. Draw us closer to You and to each other. Make our family one.

In Jesus' name, amen.

Commit to pray together at least once more this week.

DEALING WITH CONFLICT

*Do all that you can to live in peace
with everyone.*

Romans 12:18

Parenting within a blended family is much different than in a traditional family. In a blended family, besides dealing with the ordinary challenges of growing up, our children also have to contend with additional external influences. Added to the vast changes that already exist in trying to become a blended family, children of blended families experience many situations due to these outside influences that can affect their attitude within the family. This has the potential to generate a great deal of conflict in the home.

DISCOVERY

UNDERSTANDING HOW TO KEEP PEACE
IN THE HOME

Some of the outside influences in our children's lives are their other parents, their relatives, and friends and acquaintances from earlier in their lives. Any of these relationships can have a major impact on our children's efforts to integrate into our blended family. Besides these outside influences, a child's age, gender, and stage of life also have a great deal to do with how he or she adjusts to life in our home and can also contribute to the potential for family conflict.

AN ABSENT PARENT

Some children of blended families have two sets of parents who are an active part of their daily life. Both sets of parents participate in the upbringing of the child and carry similar expectations as to what they desire for the child to accomplish by adulthood. Unfortunately, this is not most commonly the case. Much more often children of blended families are raised primarily in the household of one birth parent and have little interaction with the other birth parent.

A parent who is not an active part of his or her child's day-to-day life and activities, as a parent should be, is what we call an absent parent. How do we deal with the absent parent? While there are a number of guidelines for interacting well with an absent parent, the bottom line is this: the key to raising children with an absent parent is always to seek what is in the best interest of the children. This may not always look the same from one family to another.

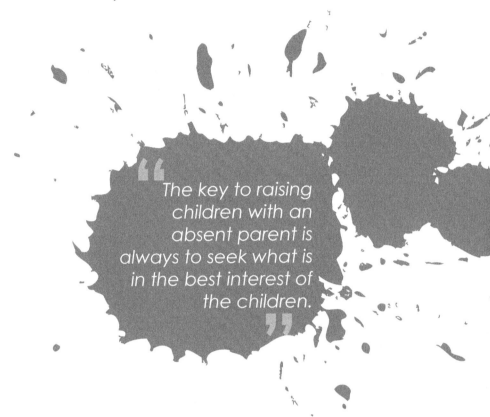

> The key to raising children with an absent parent is always to seek what is in the best interest of the children.

(For practical tips on maintaining a peaceful scenario with an absent parent, we have provided an amazing resource, "7 Ways to Deal with Conflict in Co-Parenting," that blended families may use as a tool and reference guide in learning to deal with the absent parent and the conflicts that may arise within the parenting journey.[1])

OTHER OUTSIDE INFLUENCES

Perhaps your child doesn't have an absent parent, but maybe you deal with other outside influences such as an active parent, grandparent, aunt, or uncle. All these people care about the wellbeing of your child, but they all have a different perspective on how the child should be raised. While these people are rightly part of our children's lives, it is important that we have a clear understanding of who may be influencing our children and how that influence may be impacting the dynamic of the home.

> *It is important that we have a clear understanding of who may be influencing our children and how that influence may be impacting the dynamic of the home.*

Once we establish who is influencing our children, we must become aware of what we want our children's experience in our home to look like and then set boundaries that will guard that experience.

For example, Lisa and Bill have a blended family with four children (two are Lisa's, and two are Bill's). Bill's previous wife passed away, and prior to his meeting Lisa, the children's maternal grandmother always went over and above to compensate for the children's mom being gone. Bill was fine with that and allowed the children to go to her home whenever she asked. But when Bill remarried, the children embraced Lisa and enjoyed spending time with her. Bill and Lisa and the kids began doing things as a family, and Bill had to say no at times when the grandmother asked if the kids could come over.

Over time Bill and Lisa noticed a shift in the children's attitude whenever they returned from visiting their grandmother, especially when after visits the children would go back and forth between calling Lisa "Mom" and calling her "Mrs. Lisa." One day the grandmother asked to take the children out of town for a holiday, and Bill stated no, they would be spending the holiday together as a family. The grandmother became upset and began to let Bill know how she felt.

At that moment Bill's thoughts that the children's attitudes were being influenced by the grandmother were confirmed. Bill and Lisa made a decision to restructure the relationship with his previous mother-in-law in an attempt to protect their family blending process. They did not stop the children from going to the grandmother's home, but they minimized the occurrences and maximized their family time.

A home should be a safe haven for anyone who enters, especially the people who live within it. That includes us! Every relationship isn't a healthy one for our children or for our homes. We must recognize which relationships may need some restructuring to fit the new pace and tone of our home.

HOW AGE, GENDER, AND STAGE AFFECT CHILDREN

When we (Willie and Rachel) first began blending our families, we were met with many new challenges and frustrations. Each of our children seemed to adjust differently to the new family dynamic, some better than others.

Studies have shown that children respond to the new adult in their lives differently based on age and gender. Here are some thoughts to consider from HelpGuide.org:

Kids of different ages and genders will adjust differently to a blended family. The physical and emotional needs of a two-year-old girl are different than those of a thirteen-year-old boy, but don't mistake differences in development and age for differences in fundamental needs. Just because a teenager may take a long time accepting your love and affection doesn't mean that he doesn't want it. You will need to adjust your approach with different age levels and genders, but your goal of establishing a trusting relationship is the same.[2]

The stage of life that a child is in—meaning where a child is in perceiving his or her own identity—also greatly impacts how that child will adjust to being part of a blended family. Toddlers, who receive most of their identity from parents, caregivers, and older siblings, will adjust to being part of a blended family much differently than will teenagers, who receive most of their identity from their peers and other outside influences. (For more details on how age and stage of identity affect a child's adjustment to being part of a blended family, see appendixes 1 and 2.)

When adjusting to being part of a blended family, children will take in their new situation in light of what is going on in their personal lives. Having an understanding of the ages, genders, and stages the children in your home are in will help you better understand their potential frustrations and minimize the possibility of conflict.

THE PEACE THERMOSTAT

One of the most important things that we can do is decide with our spouse where we want the "peace thermostat" of our home to be set. Many things may try to disrupt the peace within our homes, but as Romans 12:18 tells us, we are to "do all that [we] can to live in peace with everyone." This means *being intentional* to define clear ways of creating peace, and when we do this, it will help us to "reset the temperature" when it has been moved from its setting of peace.

Here are a few tips to help maintain peace in the home:

1. Have a time of family prayer every Sunday to set the thermostat for the week.

2. Have a family meeting and review the expectations for the week (regarding homework, chores, technology, etc.). Discuss how you can support each other and how everyone's roles are important to the family.

3. Have a word or phrase that everyone in your home uses when peace seems to be fading. Allow the family member who is best at keeping peace in the home to create the word. This will show your humility in admitting that you as a parent are not perfect and will allow the family member to be recognized for his or her great work in keeping peace in the home.

4. Engage in activities to help build unity in the home so that your children learn that unity and peace go hand in hand. (A good example of a fun activity is a game of volleyball, parents against kids.)

DISCUSSION:

HOW DOES THIS APPLY TO OUR SITUATION?

It's time to talk about what we've learned! Pair up with one or two other couples to answer and then discuss the questions below. (If you are uncomfortable talking with others or if you are doing this study at home, you can do this section with just your spouse.) Take ten to fifteen minutes to write your answers individually to the questions below, and then take an additional twenty to thirty minutes to discuss your answers with your spouse and the others in your group.

> *1. What are your interactions with ex-spouses, parents of your stepchildren, or in-laws like? Which relationships are healthy? Which relationships are in need of restructuring?*

2. What are some of the ways that you handle what other people say or think about your family?

3. What boundaries have you established to appropriately protect your home from outside influences? What boundaries might you need to set?

4. What ages, genders, and stages are the children in your home? How does recognizing this help you understand some of the ways your children are handling your family's blending process?

5. What temperature is your peace thermostat most commonly set on? What adjustments can you and your spouse make to reset the temperature when necessary?

APPLICATION:

WHAT WILL WE DO DIFFERENTLY NOW?

Session 2 focused on keeping peace in the home and resolving conflict in a blended family. This week, before coming back for session 3, set aside some time at home to complete the action activity below as a couple.

Each spouse should be allowed to explain his or her thoughts regarding the following questions and/or activities. Speak honestly. Listen to each other respectfully.

1. What affects the peace thermostat in your home?

2. Take a moment to evaluate your family. Identify three things that have caused conflict most often in your family (besides outside influences and children's ages, genders, and stages, this could be things like finances, discipline of children, need for intimacy, communication, faith, work, etc.). Write them below.

3. What are three strategies or steps that you will put into action to help ensure that the conflicts in your family are addressed properly? Record your answers below.

4. Revisit the family goal you made in session 1, and decide how to take an additional step to reach that goal. Before meeting for session 3, find an accountability couple and share your family goal with them.

As you wrap up your application time together as a couple, spend some time in prayer together about the developing goal you have for your family. You can close with a prayer of your own, or you can use this one:

Dear Lord,

Paul reminded the Philippians that "agreeing wholeheartedly with each other, loving one another, and working together with one mind and purpose" (2:2) is the way to achieve unity. Lord, we pray for unity in our marriage and in our family. As conflicts arise, help us to remember to seek Your will in everything. When we are divided, give us wisdom to recognize the tricks of the enemy, humility to swallow our pride, and patience to await Your response. Direct our paths, and light the way for us to be the family that You have called us to be. Make our family one.

In Jesus' name we pray, amen.

Commit to pray together at least twice more this week.

BETTER THAN MENDED

*You will live by your sword and you will serve
your brother. But when you decide to break free,
you will shake his yoke from your neck.*

Genesis 27:40

All of us have places of pain in our lives that hinder our moving forward as healthy individuals and members of our families. This week we want to begin to open up those places, seek God intensely about them, and begin healing so that we can thrive within our families as God intended.

DISCOVERY

IDENTIFYING AND BEING FREED
FROM OUR PAIN

If you and your spouse have been married for any length of time—from one day to fifty years—you know that being a blended family has its fair set of challenges, some great and some small. Sometimes these challenges become heavy weights that we carry throughout the course of our marriage.

We don't always mean to drag these frustrations and issues with us, and every once in a while we even seem to forget that they are there. Yet at any given moment, something can trigger a painful memory, and hurt can rise up within us. Suddenly we realize that we have been carrying this pain with us as a heavy weight attached to our hearts.

Before we can move forward in our journey to have a family that is better than blended, we must identify any weight that we are carrying that is affecting our relationship with our spouse, children, stepchildren, or other family members and that may be hindering us from fully embracing our blended family.

> *Before we can move forward in our journey to have a family that is better than blended, we must identify any weight that we are carrying that is affecting our relationship with our spouse, children, stepchildren, or other family members and that may be hindering us from fully embracing our blended family.*

WHAT ARE OUR SWORDS?

In Genesis 27:40, Esau's father told him, "You will live by your sword." For Esau, his sword was the hurt from his brother, Jacob, stealing the blessing that was rightfully his as the oldest brother. His father was telling him that he would choose to carry it with him.

We all carry a "sword" of some kind. Often this is something from our past, or it could be something that has happened within our blended family. The problem is, we live by the very thing that holds us captive. The swords that we hold on to within our marriage affect our actions and interactions with our spouse. They determine how we love, engage, and accept things within our lives. Unknowingly or knowingly, we filter things through the lenses of our pain. Although our swords may represent something from the past, they can become a strong part of our present and, if left unattended, will creep into our future.

Our swords shape our view of life, of family, and, more than we know, of Christ. What hurtful mindsets are you holding on to from your childhood, past relationships, or present relationships that are hindering you and your family?

WHAT ARE OUR YOKES?

Esau's father not only told his son that he would live by his sword, but also he told him, "When you decide to break free, you will shake [your brother's] yoke from your neck." A yoke binds or connects one thing to another. While a sword is something that we hold, a yoke is something that holds us. You see, as long as we hold on to our swords, we allow ourselves to be bound by a yoke.

Esau's sword was the hurt his brother had caused him, but the yoke that resulted from his hurt was unforgiveness. The yoke of unforgiveness would send Esau far away from the presence of God until he decided to let go of his sword—his hurt—and thus be freed from his yoke.

Letting go of our swords isn't always easy, but dragging a yoke along with us isn't either. Yokes can surface as physical illnesses, mental illnesses, seclusion, isolation, fighting, and much more. They have a major impact on our family and on how we embrace our children. The yokes we haul can be passed on from generation to generation.

In order to be productive members of our families, we must decide that we want our blended family to be yoke breakers, not yoke bearers. God desires for us to break free from the yoke and release our swords.

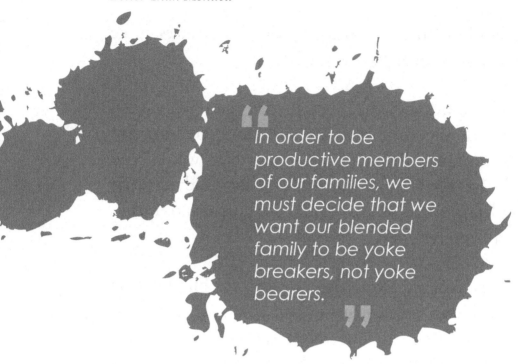

"In order to be productive members of our families, we must decide that we want our blended family to be yoke breakers, not yoke bearers."

THERE IS HEALING!

What if Esau hadn't been denied his blessing? Or what if the words that his father spoke over his life was the greater blessing? "*When you decide to break free*, you will break his yoke from your neck."

What does breaking free look like? In Esau's case it looked like forgiveness. In essence, the father was telling Esau, "When you decide to stop carrying unforgiveness toward your brother, you will have an even greater blessing." This is true in our blended families.

In order for us to experience the true blessing of being a blended family, we must decide to release the things that we have been carrying from within our family and from the past. We must decide to break free of all the swords and yokes that try to keep us from moving forward.

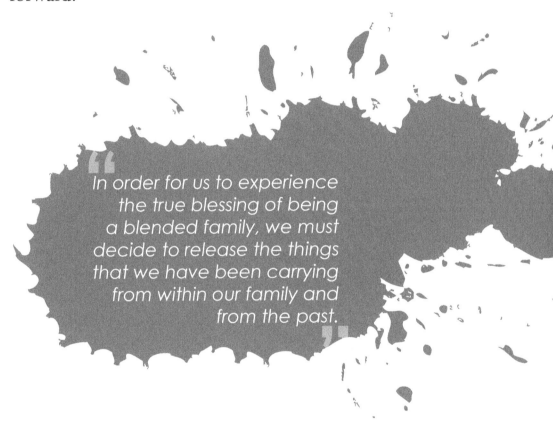

> *In order for us to experience the true blessing of being a blended family, we must decide to release the things that we have been carrying from within our family and from the past.*

This is something that no one can do for us—but when we do it, everyone will benefit from our decision, even the person or people who hurt us.

DISCUSSION:

HOW DOES THIS APPLY TO OUR SITUATION?

It's time to talk about what we've learned! Pair up with one or two other couples to answer and then discuss the questions below. (If you are uncomfortable talking with others or if you are doing this study at home, you can do this section with just your spouse.) Take ten to fifteen minutes to write your answers individually to the questions below, and then take an additional twenty to thirty minutes to discuss your answers with your spouse and the others in your group.

> *1. What swords are you holding, and what yokes are holding you because of them? In other words, if you let go of your swords, what yokes will you be freed from?*

2. What experiences from your past may cause you extreme guilt or pain every time you think of them? How are these swords and their resulting yokes affecting your family's blending process?

3. What areas within your blended family are in need of healing?

4. Who might you need to forgive or to ask forgiveness from?

5. How will forgiving others cause you to break free from your burdens? What will breaking free look and feel like for you?

APPLICATION:

WHAT WILL WE DO DIFFERENTLY NOW?

Session 3 focused on the need for healing and how it affects your blended family. This week, before coming back for session 4, set aside some time at home to complete the action activity below as a couple.

Each spouse should be allowed to explain his or her thoughts regarding the following questions and/or activities. Speak honestly. Listen to each other respectfully.

1. Healing can be instant for some, but for most it is a process. What are some actions that you will take to make sure that you are healing individually and as a family? Record your plan below.

2. Revisit the family goal you made in session 1, and decide how healing as a family will make a difference in your journey. Create a prayer journal, and record your family goal and your needs for healing in it. Share your findings with your accountability couple, and plan to check in with them frequently.

As you wrap up your application time together as a couple, spend some time in prayer together about the developing goal you have for your family. You can close with a prayer of your own, or you can use this one:

Dear Lord,

Your Word reminds us that You sent Your Word, Jesus, to heal those who cry out to You. Give us the strength to bring every wound and scar to You. Let us not be content with masking or covering our pain. Let us seek You for complete and total healing. Lord, whether we have carried our hurts for days, years, or decades, let us seek You for freedom, peace, and love. We believe in the power of Your Holy Spirit to do more than mend us—we believe You for wholeness and healing. Make our family one in You.

In Jesus' name we pray, amen.

Commit to pray together at least three more times this week.

FIGURING OUT OUR ROLES

Above all, clothe yourselves with love, which
binds us all together in perfect harmony.
Colossians 3:14

Being part of a blended family is exciting, rewarding, and confusing all at the same time. One of the greatest challenges that we face within a blended family is understanding the roles that we play in the lives of each individual family member. The role that we may have assumed we were to fulfill can quickly change to something else as we begin to better understand the personalities and needs of our spouse and children.

DISCOVERY

UNDERSTANDING THE ROLES OF SPOUSE,
PARENT, AND STEPPARENT

While every parent wears a lot of hats, becoming a blended family requires us to fill a few more roles than those required of traditional parents. Sometimes we feel pulled in various directions, and some roles can vie for dominance over others. When we identify our different roles within the family and order them correctly, it will help our marriages and families to flourish.

FOCUSING ON OUR SPOUSES

Something often forgotten in a blended family is that the most important role in the home that we are to fulfill is the role of a spouse.

It's vital that we understand this, because it's only when we clearly understand that our role as a spouse is our primary and most important role in the home that we will have the greatest impact within our family. The greatest difficulties arise when spouses don't understand this important fact.

it's only when we clearly understand that our role as a spouse is our primary and most important role in the home that we will have the greatest impact within our family.

No matter how long we were a single parent, our children must learn that they are no longer first. But most importantly, we must learn that our children are no longer first. At the point of marriage, we became one with our spouses, and that oneness should not be infiltrated.

Oneness means being accountable to one another, talking through things together, and always seeking what is best for the family before responding to a need. Making our role as spouse our primary role is something that we must constantly be working on as the demands of children and life pressure us to make our marriage secondary.

We will talk more in session 6 about ways that we can keep our marriage relationship in the forefront of our family life.

OUR RELATIONSHIP WITH OUR STEPCHILDREN

It can be a heavy weight when we try to be to our stepchildren what they don't need us to be in their lives. Sometimes we feel pressure from our spouse or from others to be what they believe is missing in a child's life. But we can quickly become overwhelmed, frustrated, and resentful because of the rejection that comes with filling a role that was never ours to fill. Let's take a step back, clear our minds of all the things that we thought we had to be in the lives of our stepchildren, such as stepmom or stepdad, and see what God has called us to be.

The Scripture tells us, "The head of every man is Christ, the head of woman is man, and the head of Christ is God" (1 Corinthians 11:3). This tells us that the head of the home is Christ and that everything else should follow suit. It is easy for us to get so wrapped up in the title of stepparents that we forget that our number-one and most important role in the lives of our stepchildren—and our biological children as well—is simply to be a godly example in the home.

In other words, we are to show them that we are striving to make Christ the head of our homes. This means that Christ's love, forgiveness, and grace should be constantly shown through us.

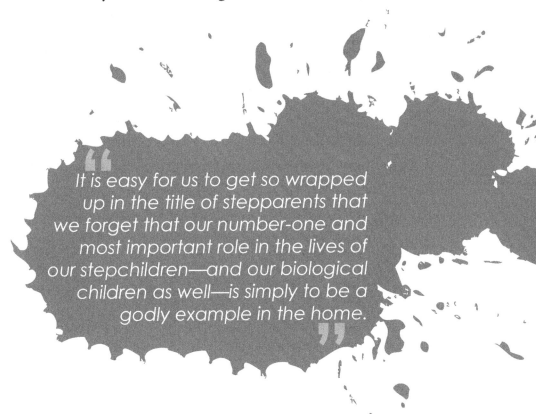

It is easy for us to get so wrapped up in the title of stepparents that we forget that our number-one and most important role in the lives of our stepchildren—and our biological children as well—is simply to be a godly example in the home.

Now this doesn't mean that we have to be perfect. It is also important that our children see our flaws and shortcomings so that they can better understand why we need a Savior; it means that as we grow in Christ, our kids should see our growth. As we draw closer to Him, they should feel it. They should be drawn to our pursuit of God because of how we live in front of them as much as by what we say to them. Our primary role in the lives of our stepchildren and children is to be a godly example.

What does it mean to be a godly example in our blended families? It simply means that we should focus on showing our stepchildren how to love in a godly way. Although they have other parents or relatives in the picture, we are the only ones who can show them how a wife should love their father in a godly way or how a husband should love their mother in a godly way. When we begin to have children together, we will be the only ones who can show our older stepchildren and children how to raise their little brothers and sisters in a godly way. No one else can stand in these places— they were specifically assigned to us—and we have the privilege of modeling Christ to our stepchildren and children through these relationships. This will be a natural relationship generator. It's as Colossians 3:14 tells us: when we clothe ourselves in love for each other, it "binds us all together in perfect harmony."

So now we have permission to take off the heavy weight of being a mom or dad to children who may not need those roles fulfilled, and instead we can just be a person who will love our stepchildren, learn about them, and give them an informal introduction to Christ.

Who better to introduce your kids to the God you know than you?

So what does love look like toward our stepchildren? Well, it looks much like the way God loves us. God never forces Himself on us—He gives us free will to serve and love Him. We see a picture of this in Jeremiah 31:3: "The Lord said to Israel: I have loved you, my people, with an everlasting love. With unfailing love I have drawn you to myself." Then, when God's great love and our free will have drawn us to Him, He leads us down a path that allows us to grow, learn, experience, and enjoy all that loving Him is about. Love does not dominate—love leads!

Love does not dominate—love leads!

The way we develop a relationship with our stepchildren is modeled through our relationship with Christ. We allow our heart for God to love our stepchildren even when they seem unlovable or don't desire our love. Then, in that moment when our love opens the door of their heart, we grow with them, learn from them, experience life with them, and enjoy them. We aren't forceful or pushy, but we are always available, understanding that love leads.

OUR RELATIONSHIP WITH OUR BIOLOGICAL CHILDREN

As we take our biological children from a state of "just us" to "all of us," we all ponder what our relationship with our biological children should look like. Becoming a blended family is a perfect opportunity to instruct our children regarding the importance of change. Children need to understand that change in life is inevitable and necessary. Yet, a change in circumstances doesn't mean a change in heart.

The best thing that we can do to continue to nurture the relationship with our children is to try not to overcompensate because they are experiencing change. Although we may feel that giving them whatever they want is the solution to how they are responding to the change, that sends them the message that when change happens, they will be rewarded for not learning to adapt to it. This is not the message we want to send our kids. Instead, we should walk with them through the change and reassure them that our love for them keeps growing every day.

Receiving reassurance in a time of change always makes the change a little more bearable. Children need to know that as they embrace the change taking place in their family, certain good things will remain the same. Even as adults we need that. Just think about a presidential debate. The candidates may have plans to change a lot of things, but the people need to know which good things they plan to keep from our current government. So our relationship with our biological children should be one of continuously growing love, understanding, patience, and encouragement to embrace the new.

DISCUSSION:

HOW DOES THIS APPLY TO OUR SITUATION?

It's time to talk about what we've learned! Pair up with one or two other couples to answer and then discuss the questions below. (If you are uncomfortable talking with others or if you are doing this study at home, you can do this section with just your spouse.) Take ten to fifteen minutes to write your answers individually to the questions below, and then take an additional twenty to thirty minutes to discuss your answers with your spouse and the others in your group.

1. What expectations have been placed on you in regards to being a stepparent? How have those expectations made you feel?

2. How would you define your role as a stepparent? How do you think your stepchildren feel about being part of a blended family?

3. How do you think your biological children feel about you being part of a stepfamily?

4. What can you do to help foster your relationship with your biological children as well as with your stepchildren?

5. How can you reassure your biological children of what will remain the same about your relationship with them?

APPLICATION:

WHAT WILL WE DO DIFFERENTLY NOW?

Session 4 focused on finding your role in a blended family. This week, before coming back for session 5, set aside some time at home to complete the action activity below as a couple.

Each spouse should be allowed to explain his or her thoughts regarding the following questions and/or activities. Speak honestly. Listen to each other respectfully.

1. Discuss with your spouse plans for a family activity that will help bring some of your children's needs and questions out into the open and draw your family together:

- *Schedule time for a family day.*

- *Find an activity or a game, such as Monopoly, that takes time and will allow for family discussion during the game.*

- *Have a meal prepared after the activity or game and plan for everyone to sit together to talk and be open with each other about what challenges they may be facing with blending and what they feel would help them during this process.*

- *Be sure to acknowledge each one's feelings, but speak life to each person as well.*

2. Do an activity together to prepare for next week's session. Go online and visit Active Parent Publishing at http://www.activeparenting.com/Parents-Parenting_Style_Quiz and take the quiz you find there. What is your parenting style—aggressive or passive? What is your spouse's parenting style? Write this down for each of you and discuss it together before attending session 5 next week.

3. Revisit the family goal you made in session 1, and create a family values statement answering the question, "What characteristics define our family?" Decide where to display this document in your home. Update your prayer journal with additional needs and/or answered prayer regarding your family goal. Share your prayers with your accountability couple.

As you wrap up your application time together as a couple, spend some time in prayer together about the developing goal you have for your family. You can close with a prayer of your own, or you can use this one:

Dear Lord,

We thank You for the fresh start that You offer to each believer, and we are grateful for the fresh start that You are making available to our family. Help us to grow in love and mutual respect for one another. Help us to learn about each other as we learn from each other. Show us how to handle conflict and celebrate success together as a family. In the times when we are certain of Your direction and the times where we feel unsure, our prayer remains the same: make us one family in You.

In Jesus' name we pray, amen.

Commit to pray together at least four more times this week.

DISCIPLINE MEANS DISCIPLESHIP

Direct your children onto the right path, and
when they are older, they will not leave it.

Proverbs 22:6

Frustrations can arise when we blend a family and don't consider some of the practical things that should be adjusted because of the new family dynamic— things like schedules, activities, and boundaries. When we set out to become better than blended, it is vital that we reassess our family priorities and make adjustments where necessary to help our homes run more smoothly. In other words, we need to set some rules.

Some of this is just practical common sense—after all, we need to keep track of who is going where and doing what. But setting guidelines in the home is about more than keeping order. It's about training our children to be disciplined, obedient, and godly. It's about discipleship.

DISCOVERY
RAISING CHILDREN TO BECOME
GODLY ADULTS

As we work intentionally toward unity in our blended family, we need to consider a major factor: not all children are alike. In fact, they are all uniquely different, and with their different personalities come differences in personal needs. When it comes to blended families, one size does not fit all.

ONE SIZE DOESN'T FIT ALL

Let's take a look at some things blended families may need to consider adjusting:

- *School.* Some children do best in public schools, while others thrive at home school or in a private school. Consider what will be best for each individual child in this important area of their lives.

- *Church.* Taking into consideration the best place for your family to fellowship is vitally important. The church you attended before you married may not work with your new family dynamics. You will want to find a place where everyone can be built up and grow in the Word of God. Seek God, and ask Him to lead you to the right place to fellowship.

- *Bedtimes.* Agreeing upon a time when you and your spouse would like everyone to be in bed is important. The best way to set this up when you have children of different ages is to do a staggered bedtime. This will allow the older kids to feel as if they have received special privileges and will give the younger kids something to look forward to in the future. Stagger the bedtimes starting from the time you would like everyone to be in bed. If that time is eight o'clock, then the youngest should start to go to bed at seven, while the oldest children should have until eight.

- *Outside activities.* Some children enjoy sports, while others enjoy just hanging out with friends. Understanding that each child is unique will help you not to feel that you have to do something for one child just because you did it for another. Some activities cost more than others and require more time. If your goal is to support each child, then understand that this support will look different for each one. For one it may require more of a monetary element, while for another it may require showing up to his or her performance.

WHAT ARE OUR PARENTING STYLES?

While it is helpful for us to adjust family schedules and activities, things will not go smoothly all the time. In the course of family life, we will inevitably have to deal with behavioral issues in our children, and it's important for us to consider the best way to do that.

The beautiful thing, when a couple decides to get married, is that two people from two different walks of life come together to live life together. The challenge, however, is that two different people from two different walks of life come together under one roof to live life together! Do you see the problem as it relates to parenting? Two people who have been parented by different people will have different parenting styles. Our parenting style is a mixture of how we were raised (our parents' style), what we like and dislike about how we were parented, and what we have learned along the way from our own life experiences.

One of the most important things we can do is understand our own parenting style. Are we a passive parent or a strong disciplinarian? There are many resources that can help us learn our parenting style. One useful free tool, as we saw in the previous session's "Application" section, is a quiz created by Active Parenting Publishers. (If you did not do this quiz in advance of today's session, stop to do it now, if the class structure allows for it. If it does not, you can carry on with the session and do the quiz later at http://www.activeparenting.com/Parents-Parenting_Style_Quiz.)

" One of the most important things we can do is understand our own parenting style. "

Once we figure out whether we have a passive or authoritarian parenting style, it's important to discover whether or not our style works within our home and, if it doesn't, to find out what other styles should be considered. It is so easy for us to fall into the trap of parenting in the same way that we were raised or, on the other hand, attempting to parent in the complete opposite direction, only to find out that in the end our methods were not best for our children.

As parents, we need to take time to gauge what is working in our home, because the goal of parenting is to raise godly children to become godly adults and to prepare them for life outside the home so that they can become well-rounded citizens within society. We can know whether or not our parenting style is working if the way we are parenting provides our kids with what they need to fulfill these goals.

DISCIPLINE—PUNISHMENT OR DISCIPLESHIP?

It is important as a couple for us to handle our children's behavioral issues in a way that leaves both spouses comfortable. In order to do this, we need to talk about our personal expectations as to how we should respond to our children's behavior. In a home that is being guided by the goal of becoming better than blended, the word "discipline" actually means "discipleship." These two words look and sound similar—and that is because they are. The problem is, we often misunderstand the true meaning of the word "discipline." Take a look at the differing views below:

- *Discipline as punishment.* This view is more focused on a child's behavior as the issue and on providing a reaction to an action, which often means punishing simply for the sake of punishing. The focus of this example is solely to dole out consequences, regardless of their actual impact on the child's behavior.

- *Discipline as discipleship.* This view pursues the root of a child's behavior and not just the behavior itself. Discipleship considers why the behavior took place, what lesson needs to be learned, and what needs to be done to see the behavior changed. The focus of this approach is correction that may result in a consequence that is unpleasing to the child but that will change the child's behavior.

Jesus' focus with His disciples was to teach them the right way to live so that they would correct their sinful behavior. Discipleship in the lives of our children should have a similar focus. When we allow discipleship to guide us in handling behavioral issues within the home, we avoid reacting in the moment and instead seek God on how to respond to the situation.

Then as a couple we can decide to be open to trying new things as we allow discipleship to take the lead!

This is what the writer of Proverbs is driving home when he instructs us, "Direct your children onto the right path, and when they are older, they will not leave it" (Proverbs 22:6). This simple truth about discipleship will help us set our children on the right path toward becoming godly children within our home.

DISCUSSION:

HOW DOES THIS APPLY TO OUR SITUATION?

It's time to talk about what we've learned! Pair up with one or two other couples to answer and then discuss the questions below. (If you are uncomfortable talking with others or if you are doing this study at home, you can do this section with just your spouse.) Take ten to fifteen minutes to write your answers individually to the questions below, and then take an additional twenty to thirty minutes to discuss your answers with your spouse and the others in your group.

> *1. What are some areas of your blended-family life in which you need to realize that one size doesn't fit all?*

2. What was your parents' style of parenting—passive or authoritarian?

3. What is your parenting style, and from what sources do you think this was adapted?

4. How do you and your spouse currently handle behavioral issues within your home?

5. How can your methods of discipline be changed to better foster the goals of raising godly children to become godly adults and to prepare them for life outside the home so that they can become well-rounded citizens within society?

APPLICATION:

WHAT WILL WE DO DIFFERENTLY NOW?

Session 5 focused on discipline versus discipleship. This week, before coming back for session 6, set aside some time at home to complete the action activity below as a couple.

Each spouse should be allowed to explain his or her thoughts regarding the following questions and/or activities. Speak honestly. Listen to each other respectfully.

1. Discuss as a couple how your parenting styles have impacted your relationship with each other positively or negatively.

2. Talk about the kinds of responses to behavioral issues that you are comfortable with versus the kinds you're not comfortable with. Explain to your spouse the reason you feel this way.

3. Come up with two or three ways in which you can respond to issues with the goal of discipline as discipleship rather than discipline as punishment.

Write your answers below.

4. Revisit the family goal you made in session 1, and think about how God has moved in your marriage and family during the past five weeks. Record your reflections in your prayer journal. How would you like to see God move in the next five weeks? Pray boldly together. Share your prayers with your accountability couple.

As you wrap up your application time together as a couple, spend some time in prayer together about the developing goal you have for your family. You can close with a prayer of your own, or you can use this one:

Dear Lord,

You made each of us unique. You created each of us differently. We are fearfully and wonderfully made by Your hand. Let us treasure our differences and trust Your creative ingenuity as we seek to honor Your work in each of our family members. Thank You for making us in Your image. Help us to be disciplined in our lives and to let our lives serve as a tool to disciple others. Make us one family in You.

In Jesus' name we pray, amen.

Commit to pray together at least five more times this week.

MAKING TIME FOR FAMILY TOGETHERNESS

I want them to be encouraged and knit together

by strong ties of love.

Colossians 2:2

We have spent five weeks discussing ways to become better than blended, and for our final week, we are going to talk about ways to stay better than blended. The key to a peaceful, joyous blended family is to love each other intentionally and, in so doing, to create a story that can be shared together for years to come. We do this by deliberately making time to be together in enjoyable and meaningful ways.

As families invest in experiencing life together, they will grow together, love each other more deeply, and bond with each other. All these are essential elements to being a family that will want to be around each other later. We don't want our families to just exist and tolerate each other but to live with and love one another now as well as when they grow older!

DISCOVERY

CREATING WAYS TO BOND AS A FAMILY

Family time can take many forms—sometimes fun, other times more serious. Both are important. Let's look at several ways that we can make time for family togetherness and deepen our family relationships.

FINDING TIME FOR FUN!

What better way to bond and become closer as a family than to have fun together? This could mean anything from playing outside in the yard or at a park to playing board games around the kitchen table. The goal isn't about what we do but about growing closer because we are doing it.

As we make time for our family to have fun together, we create memories that will last a lifetime. Making memories can happen by accident, but they should happen on purpose. When we spend time together with our families, we need to make each moment count. Being intentional now will produce a later harvest of well-nurtured relationships and friendships within the family.

"Making memories can happen by accident, but they should happen on purpose."

Making memories can include things like going on family vacations or creating holiday traditions. It could mean baking cookies, doing a craft project, or just being willing to play hide-and-seek or Legos with your kids. All these things give the family members something to talk about later and memories to carry with them as they grow up.

KEEPING THE ROMANTIC FLAME BURNING

As we mentioned in session 4, outside of our relationship with God, our marriage is our priority relationship. Many times we become so focused on blending with the children and learning about them that we forget to invest in learning about and spending time with our spouse. But no matter how busy life gets and how many demands are placed upon us, we need to always remember that our first priority relationship is with our spouse.

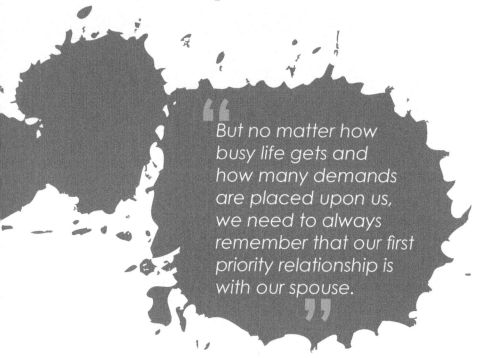

> *But no matter how busy life gets and how many demands are placed upon us, we need to always remember that our first priority relationship is with our spouse.*

To make our spouse our number-one priority in the family, sometimes we have to remind ourselves that we are parents to x number of kids but the husband or wife of just one person. This means that we have to be intentional with our marriage relationship, because it can easily fall to the bottom of the list. It is our job to preserve our marriage and to be proactive in making time for our spouse.

How do we preserve our marriages as our priority relationship? Here are some tips:

1. Put God first. He should be Lord of your life and your marriage.

2. Set time aside each evening for you and your spouse to talk to each other about your day.

3. Be open to what your spouse needs.

4. Listen attentively to what's going on in your spouse's life.

5. Hire a reliable babysitter for date nights.

6. Plan date nights—and stick to them.

7. Plan a night away (or a few nights) to rekindle the flames.

8. Learn about something that interests your spouse so that you can engage in his or her interest.

9. Flirt with each other as much as possible.

10. Make communication a priority.

PRAYING TOGETHER

We have made it to the final step to becoming better than blended! Although prayer is first in importance in building a godly family, we put it last in our workbook so that the matter of prayer would be fresh in our minds as we finish this study.

> *Prayer is first in importance in building a godly family.*

Prayer in a family does many things. It protects the family unity, reminds the enemy that he is defeated, teaches our children that every good and perfect gift comes from above (see James 1:17), and much more. It is also the ultimate means of drawing us close together as a family so that we will remain "encouraged and knit together by strong ties of love" (Colossians 2:2).

Prayer is your family's proclamation!

As our family becomes one and we pursue something better than what we may have been told about how blended families work, what we experienced from our own blended family when we were growing up, or what we may have feared in the past about being a blended family, we must continue to seek the face of the One who holds the world in His hand.

DISCUSSION:

HOW DOES THIS APPLY TO OUR SITUATION?

It's time to talk about what we've learned! Pair up with one or two other couples to answer and then discuss the questions below. (If you are uncomfortable talking with others or if you are doing this study at home, you can do this section with just your spouse.) Take ten to fifteen minutes to write your answers individually to the questions below, and then take an additional twenty to thirty minutes to discuss your answers with your spouse and the others in your group.

1. What does your family do for fun?

2. Do you and your spouse have a regular date night? How do you make sure that you protect your time together as a couple?

3. How often do you pray together as a couple? As a family? What can you do to ensure that you will have regular time in prayer?

4. What topic from this study has been most impactful for your family?

5. What changes have you seen in your family over the past six weeks? What changes are you most looking forward to in the future?

APPLICATION:

WHAT WILL WE DO DIFFERENTLY NOW?

Session 6 focused on finding time for fun. As this study comes to an end, it is important to prioritize ways for you and your spouse as well as for your entire family to enjoy spending time together. This week, set aside some time at home to complete the application activity below as a couple.

Each spouse should be allowed to explain his or her thoughts regarding the following questions and/ or activities. Speak honestly. Listen to each other respectfully.

1. Plan a family activity, and chronicle the activity with pictures: cook a meal, plan a scavenger hunt, play a game, put on a play, or come up with some other creative idea. Use your creativity to create a unique experience that will help your family grow closer to each other. Enjoy the process!

2. Be intentional about planning a regular family prayer time. This could be every night before bed, in the morning before everyone leaves for work and/or school, or any time that works well for your family.

3. Revisit the family goal you made in session 1, and think about how God has moved in your family during the past six weeks. What dreams do you have for your family? Record it in your prayer journal. Share

your testimony and dreams with your accountability couple.

As you wrap up your application time together as a couple, spend some time in prayer together about the developing goal you have for your family. You can close with a prayer of your own, or you can use this one:

Dear Lord,

Blend our family into what You have called us to be. Help us to remember to seek Your truth for our identity. In conflict let us seek the gift of Your peace. When we are wounded, let us come to You to find healing. Make us into new creatures who find our true roles and callings in You alone. Let us welcome Your discipline so that we can disciple our families and all who witness our walk with You. As we become who You have called us to be as a family, may we enjoy and value fun together as a family. Help us to be intentional. Help us to be one family in You. Help us to be better than blended.

In Jesus' name we pray, amen.

Commit to pray together at least six more times this week.

LEADER'S GUIDE

The *Better than Blended Workbook* is a six-week study course for couples who are parenting blended families and who desire, with God's help, to do the best job they can building a unified blended family that doesn't just survive but also thrives! The study is intended to be done in a group setting with a leader (although it can work equally well in a small group of several couples or even with a single couple at home).

This study presents six sessions that cover various topics facing blended families:

1. Discovering their own unique blended-family story

2. Dealing with conflict that can develop in a blended family

3. Healing from past hurts so that they can grow their family in a healthy way

4. Defining their various roles, such as spouse, parent, and stepparent

5. Learning the biblical meaning of discipline (it's not about punishment!)

6. Exploring various ways to create family togetherness and closeness

You, the leader, will have a certain amount of freedom in directing the study as needed for your group. Guidelines are given below, but room is left for you to be sensitive to your group's needs and to the Holy Spirit's direction.

Make sure that every person has his or her own copy of the *Better than Blended Workbook*, a Bible, and a pen or a pencil.

Each session is broken into three sections:

- Discovery
- Discussion
- Application

Discovery (30–45 minutes). This first section is one of your biggest responsibilities as a leader. During this time you will lead the couples attending the study through the teaching presented in each session. The text in the "Discovery" section of the workbook provides the basis for the teaching.

We encourage you to study the material in advance and be prepared to present the teaching along with comments and scriptural applications of your own. Or, if you are uncomfortable adding your own commentary to the teaching, you could simply read the text aloud and have the couples read along silently with you. This second option won't fill the time allotted for this section, but you can extend the time by giving couples freedom to interject comments and ask questions as you read.

Discussion (30–45 minutes). Direct the couples to break into groups of two to three couples each for a time of answering questions and discussing the material presented in the "Discovery" section. If a couple is uncomfortable sharing openly with others in the group, they can work as a single couple.

Instruct the couples to spend the first ten to fifteen minutes of the "Discussion" section writing their answers to the questions listed in their workbooks. Following that, they should spend the next twenty to thirty minutes discussing their answers with the other couples in their group.

If the couples are engaging with each other and profitably sharing, the discussion time can be extended beyond the thirty to forty-five minutes as you see fit.

When time is up or when discussion seems to be winding down, call the group back together to finish the session.

Application. This final section is for the couples to do at home together. It includes a question or a challenge of some kind as well as an activity. It ends with a time of prayer. Read the "Application" instructions aloud with the group, and be sure everyone understands the assignment. Encourage couples to commit to praying with each other during the week, and encourage them to increase this time each week so that they grow in the habit of praying together as a couple for their marriage and for their family.

Close the session by leading the group in prayer.

A FEW PRACTICAL TIPS

Leading a group gives you an important opportunity to help others grow, and at times, to evangelize. Knowing that you cannot produce growth in others by your own strength, you must find your equipping and guidance in the Lord. Before starting the study, take time to pray for your group.

As you get a sense of God's direction for the group, consider adding different elements to your meetings.

Small groups are perfect settings not just for Bible study but also for making friends, having a safe place to open up, sharing needs, praying with other believers, and worshiping together. It's also a good venue for reaching out to new friends. So think about how you may want to spend time in fellowship: singing, sharing, or praying.

Everyone has a different idea of punctuality these days, but as the leader, it's your job to keep things running smoothly. Starting on time, or after a reasonable time of fellowship, helps get the group focused so that you can make the best use of your time.

As you lead the study, don't be afraid of silence—or of controversy. Every group responds and interacts differently. Take things slowly and give people time to think and listen. Then look to Scripture for answers and ask God for wisdom. He will show you how to keep things moving or bring things back on topic.

Remember too that a study of this nature is intended to provoke discussion. While the "Discovery" section of the session is largely led by you, the leader, for the "Discussion" section you become a facilitator. Encourage couples to open up, share, and ask questions.

As the couples work through the questions in the "Discussion" section, give them plenty of time to answer the questions and respond to each other's findings. Leave room for freedom and for the working of the Holy Spirit in people's hearts. Be open to adjusting the meeting's schedule if you sense God is addressing particular needs.

It probably goes without saying, but spending time in prayer together will have a valuable impact in peoples' lives. However you want to schedule it into the study, making time for the couples to pray together about things they are learning, about their questions, and about challenges they'll face in applying the material could be a big blessing to the group. Even beyond that, we encourage you to have someone available to pray with the couples as different issues arise, and also to have resources within or outside the church to give to the couples as they begin to open up about needs in their lives. (For a good list of resources, see "Resources" at the end of this book.)

Encourage the group members to pray for each other during the week as well. Their fellowship and spiritual growth will develop further as they commit to praying for each other's personal needs.

Thank you for your willingness to lead couples through the *Better than Blended Workbook!* May God bless these sessions and each one participating in them for His glory.

APPENDIX 1

How Different Ages Affect Children's Adjustment to Blended Families

Young children under 10:

- May adjust more easily because they thrive on cohesive family relationships.
- Are more accepting of a new adult.
- Feel competitive for their parent's attention.
- Have more daily needs to be met.

Adolescents aged 10 to 14:

- May have the most difficult time adjusting to a stepfamily.
- Need more time to bond before accepting a new person as a disciplinarian.
- May not demonstrate their feelings openly but may be as sensitive, or more sensitive, than young children when it comes to needing love, support, discipline, and attention.

Teenagers 15 or older:

- May have less involvement in stepfamily life.
- Prefer to separate from the family as they form their own identities.
- Also may not be open in their expression of affection or sensitivity but still want to feel important, loved, and secure.

Gender differences—general tendencies:

- Both boys and girls in stepfamilies tend to prefer verbal affection, such as praises or compliments, rather than physical closeness, like hugs and kisses.
- Girls tend to be uncomfortable with physical displays of affection from their stepfather.
- Boys seem to accept a stepfather more quickly than girls.

Please note that these are only generalizations. Each blended-family experience may be very similar or very different, but understanding these basic principles will help guide our family expectations.[1]

APPENDIX 2

How Different Stages of Identity Affect Children's Adjustment to Blended Families

Infants and toddlers 0–4 years old. In this stage children are likely to associate most strongly with the parental figures in their lives. Parents, caregivers, and older siblings help to mold their view of life and who they are. Toddlers will mimic behavior to help shape their identity. Having the love, acceptance, and admiration of their parental figures is an important element to their proper growth and to shaping who they are. This stage is very relationship driven.

Young children 5–12 years old. At this stage children still tend to mimic their parental figures but are now greatly influenced by friends and other outside influences. They are seeking a greater understanding of who they are and who they desire to become based on the people, places, and things that surround them. They are more likely to express the attitudes and behaviors of people with whom they have relationships or toward whom they gravitate. While young children take the opinions and ideas of others and own them as their own, they remain open to wisdom from their parental figures. They are still developing their understanding of right and wrong. They are learning a lot about relationships through both visual and auditory means.

Teens. In this stage young people are less connected to their parental figures and instead seek their identity from outside influences. They are more likely to disengage from conversation and develop their own attitude about life as it exists. Much of their interaction with family members will be brief and basic—they often won't open up too much about how they feel or what they are thinking regarding life. Teens' moods are ever changing. In this stage they become visual learners when it comes to understanding relationships. In other words, they are less moved by what they hear people say and more by what they see.

NOTES

Session 2: Dealing with Conflict

1. Rachel Scott, *7 Ways To Deal With Conflict In Co-Parenting*, www.7WaysToDealWithConflictInCoParenting.com

2. Gina Kemp, MA, Jeanne Segal, PhD, and Lawrence Robinson, "Step-Parenting and Blended Families,"HelpGuide.org, September 2015, http://www.helpguide.org/articles/family-divorce/step-parenting-blended-families.htm.

Appendix 1: How Different Ages Affect Children's Adjustment to Blended Families

1. Gina Kemp, MA, Jeanne Segal, PhD, and Lawrence Robinson, "Step-Parenting and Blended Families," HelpGuide.org, September 2015, http://www.helpguide.org/articles/family-divorce/step-parenting-blended- families.htm.

RESOURCES

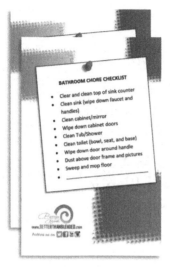

CHORE CHECKLIST
How many of us have had to sit down and have the frustrating conversation with our children about how they AREN'T doing the chores correctly? You can tell them how to wipe that spot on the glass 100 times and you will go back to the window and the entire window will be wiped down BUT that spot. WHY? To drive you crazy of course! Well here are some helpful tools you can use to encourage proper home cleaning. You can cater these lists to your specific taste or home needs but these are great tools to assist you in teaching your children that "we honor God by taking care of everything He blesses us with."

Log onto the website and get your FREE download of our various "Chore Checklists."

7 WAYS TO DEAL WITH CONFLICT IN CO-PARENTING
7 Proven Strategies to Help You Find Peace Where Conflict Exists

When conflict comes to us, it's easy to feel a need to respond saying exactly how we feel. I believe this is a natural human response, especially when you feel it's an attack on your parenting (be it true or untrue). It wasn't until my friend encouraged me to respond to all of the nasty text messages with a simple 'OK' or by not saying anything at all, I was able to defuse the conflict. Saying nothing was like watching a balloon blow up and letting go of the end to watch the air seep slowly out of it. It had no place to go, but away.

The high-conflict parent thrives off of your responses and when you don't give any after a few tries, they stop fighting in the ring alone. *"7 Ways To Deal With Conflict In Co-Parenting"* gives you practical ways and real-life scenarios in an effort to bring control and peace of mind back into your interaction.

RESOURCES

Below is a list of websites that have been a help to us in our own blended-family journey. We hope that they will be a help to you as well!

Journey Community Church: www.journeypeople.com

Lastleaf: www.lastleaf.org

HelpGuide.org: www.helpguide.org

Active Parenting Publishers: www.activeparenting.com

Laugh Your Way to a Better Marriage: www.markgungor.com

Lifeway Covenant Fellowship: www.lifeway.org

StepMom Magazine: www.stepmommag.com

Moody Radio: www.moodyradio.com

Rightnow Media: www.rightnowmedia.com

Café Smom: www.wordpress.cafesmom.com

Datebox at www.getdatebox.com

The Joyful Stepmom at www.thejoyfulstepmom.com

Thank you for using the *Better than Blended Workbook* as a resource guide to becoming a stronger family unit. We hope and pray that it has made and will continue to make a difference in the interactions between you and your spouse and with your children. We also pray that it has encouraged you to be intentional with each family interaction and to seek God in everything.

For more information on blended-family resources or to book Willie and Rachel to speak at your church or venue, visit:

www.BETTERTHANBLENDED.com

or e-mail us at

info@betterthanblended.com

Please follow, share, and comment on our social media sites:

www.facebook.com/betterthanblended
www.twitter.com/BetterThanBlend

Made in the USA
Columbia, SC
24 February 2018